THE
LEMON
BOOK

"Mother Nature's Cure-All For Everyday Problems"

THE LEMON BOOK

Ray Collins

Copyright (c) 2007 The Good Life Letter Ltd

Published 2007 by The Good Life Letter Ltd

The Good Life Letter Ltd

New Court, Abbey Road North

Shepley, Huddersfield, HD8 8BJ

www.goodlifeletter.co.uk

ISBN 978-0-9557324-0-9

CONTENTS

WARNING

The publishers have carefully checked the contents of *The Lemon Book* to ensure that it's as accurate as possible at the time of publication.

That said, please be advised that the information in these pages is not necessarily representative of health professionals and physicians. Please don't treat it as a substitute for medical advice from qualified doctors.

If you are pregnant, we advise that you seek professional advice before making any dietary changes.

You should seek medical attention in all emergencies, such as accidents, high fever or heart attack. If you are worried that you have a serious illness, please consult a medical professional first.

This book is here to educate people about the many little-known benefits of lemon and ginger.

Neither the author nor the publishers can accept legal responsibility for any problems that may occur with trying the ideas, tips and recommendations in this book.

About the Author:

A One-Man Information Revolution!

R ay Collins is the researcher behind *The Good Life Letter* (www.goodlifeletter.co.uk) a free online resource for anyone who's interested in alternative remedies, nutrition and the health stories the mainstream media never tell you.

His website, and the free email newsletter that goes with it, has been around since 2005. And it's still going strong.

Not surprising, considering that Ray's a one-man information revolution! After hours of painstaking research each week, Ray fills his newsletters with useful tips, ideas, rants and hilarious stories of media hypocrisy and hysteria. It's his mission to sift the truth from the nonsense, and seek out extraordinary health revelations like:

• The shocking truth about your heart – and a vitamin that could turn around your health in weeks...
• How to breathe more easily with white wine and chocolate...

- A natural vitamin bath that could help slow the effects of age-related blindness...
- How to improve your eyesight and fight cataracts with jam...
- How to beat your headache without expensive tablets...
- The cheese that could be good for your heart...
- How a type of tree bark can ease asthma – and how Eastern European salt could mean drug-free relief for all sorts of breathing problems...

Ray isn't a do-gooder doctor, scientist or a medical bore. He's a normal family guy who is on a quest to find out how ordinary, everyday foods can help us fight disease and life longer, happier lives.

To browse his free website or receive his free, twice-weekly emails, go to:

www.goodlifeletter.co.uk

Introduction

I hope you get as much out of reading this book as I have from writing it. Because I believe that what you have in your hands is more than simply a "book about lemons". It's about living a more natural life.

By the time you've finished reading, your head should be buzzing with hundreds of ideas about how you can change the way you eat, clean your home, buy food, and treat everyday ailments.

Your home will smell fresher. The air you breathe will be healthier. You'll be more environmentally friendly. You'll be less susceptible to the many health threats of the 21st century. And you'll have saved possibly hundreds of pounds on unnecessary and wasteful products.

Now, I'm not pretending that this is some kind of science book or doctor's manual. Thank goodness, really, because I'm neither a doctor, nor a scientist. I'm just an ordinary guy who's dedicated the last couple of years digging up extraordinary nuggets of information from books, science journals, websites, newsletters, and even forums where people pass on their tips and knowledge.

My mission has been to find inexpensive, natural and easy ways to improve our lives in many ways. But rather than follow what the mainstream press or big businesses TELL us is good for us, I've decided to open my mind and take my own path.

I am a self-confessed information junkie. And I look everywhere...

Old folk remedies, Chinese medicine, modern scientific breakthroughs, alternative therapies, cutting-edge revelations that haven't yet hit the news papers, forgotten herbal treatments used hundreds of years ago, old wives' tales that really work, secrets handed down through generations... you name it, I've looked into it. Probed it. Investigated further. Turned it upside down, and looked at it all over again.

If you keep an open mind, it will amaze you how wondrous and powerful are the gifts of Mother Nature. Which is a good thing too. Because in these times of artificial products, environmental pollution, food processing and expensive drugs, it's never been more important to remember the easily-available products that grow from trees or sprout from the ground.

I should know, because it was my own loved ones who spurred me to create my website, www.goodlifeletter.co.uk and write this book.

Let me introduce myself...

How my family taught me to look deeper into natural remedies and treatments

My name is Ray Collins. (I have a middle name as well, but that's best left alone.) I'm a shade over six foot, a little overweight, and with all the aches and creaks associated with a middle-aged man. I used to play rugby at university, and picked up a fair few injuries along the way, including a neck problem that still troubles me from time to time. I like my wine, cheese, red meat and the occasional cigar.

You could say, I'm no goody two shoes. Never have been. I've lived the high life, and in my time I've eaten fast food, sprayed my home with chemicals to get rid of that "rugby sock" smell and wasted money I didn't have on expensive products I didn't need.

Know the kind of thing I'm talking about? Anything for an easy time.

Well, that was Yours Truly. But then, to my surprise and delight, I got married and had children. My family taught me how fragile and precious our health and homes can be.

As I've got older, and a little wiser, I've realised that the buck stops with me. Their well-being is my responsibility. Not with the medical establishment. Not with what I can pick up in daily newspapers. And not with the drug companies.

It's up to us to ensure we enjoy healthy, happy, stress-free lives

You and I, we share a goal. To live long, happy lives, and to give our friends and families the very best we have to offer. And we want to do it without breaking the bank, going into debt, ruining our health, or wrecking the world around us. Right?

The trouble is, if you read the papers or watch the news, you're bombarded with scare stories and revelations. Every day it seems we are told something new is bad for us, or bad for the environment. There's so much confusion in the mainstream media about what to eat and what not to eat. Worse still, much of the press is biased towards mega-corporations and their clinical trials. Big business rules the roost these days, I'm sad to say.

So what's the truth? What are you supposed to clean your home with? What are you supposed to eat? What are you supposed to avoid at all costs?

More importantly, how can you tell if the information you are being given is purely for your own benefit or if it's being driven by profits? There's so much money in cleaning products, processed foods and conventional medicines, you could hardly blame the business side of things for – shall we say – encouraging you to part with your money.

Take the humble lemon, for example. It's natural. It grows on trees. It costs pennies in the local shop. And yet, in its natural form, it has incredible cleaning and healing powers.

Just add it to water, squeeze it, eat it, cook with it. No processing necessary.

Imagine if a corporation invented the lemon. It would be patented, marketed and sold around the world for billions of pounds. But they can't do that to a fruit. So often they look for artificial equivalents of the same thing. And you don't really get told much these days about natural foods and how effective they really are – especially for the niggly problems of everyday life.

Sometimes, we simply don't NEED artificial products. They're often a waste of time and money. They can even damage our health.

Now it's time to fight back – by seeking knowledge

When I began looking into natural health remedies, I soon discovered many little-known and forgotten natural remedies for common ailments. Something as cheap as the lemon can be even better for you than many pricey medicines you get at the chemist.

Now, please understand. In no way am I denying the progress of science or the amazing things the medical establishment can do, or that there are powerful and important drugs and procedures that save lives.

But what I can do is tilt the balance a bit.

This book is my attempt to gather together every single titbit of information I've found on the benefits of the humble lemon. I've not censored it according to my beliefs or prejudices. I've not worried about going into relentless details. I have simply found out as much as I possibly can and presented it in this book in a clear, fun, readable way.

This is for your information only. It's not medical advice. It's a way to provide you with ideas, new insights and inspiration. And, hopefully, entertain you too.

But I promise, you'll be BLOWN AWAY by the hundreds of ways a lemon could improve your life. For centuries it's been used as a powerful health remedy... stress reliever... home cleaner... magic stain remover... insect repellent... beauty enhancer... protector against disease... and even a way to slow the effects of ageing.

Best of all, it's 100% natural, and will cost you only a few pennies at your local shop.

You could say that it's Mother Nature's secret "cure-all".

In this book you'll see how good health and a clean home doesn't have to cost you a lot of hassle or money. Lemons can replace those expensive, toxin-laden cleaning products in your cupboards. They can save you hundreds of pounds on health supplements and medicines, and outperform many overpriced beauty products.

Prepare for great little tips, like how a lemon can...

- Safely bleach your wooden chopping boards
- Clean kitchen surfaces without nasty, abrasive chemicals
- Remove unpleasant odours from your fridge, instantly and easily
- Remove limescale from your taps, dissolve soap scum and hard water deposits
- Shine all your brass, aluminium and copper
- Naturally and effectively scrub all your dishes without risk
- Remove ink, rust, or mild stains from clothes
- Polish your hardwood furniture
- Scrub those stained plastic storage containers in your cupboards
- Freshen your drains and your kitchen
- Freshen the air throughout your home
- Clean and deodorise your microwave

You'll save a whole pile of cash. And not a grim chemical in sight.

You can use lemon to heal, treat and prevent many illnesses

You'll see dozens of little-known ways that a lemon could...

- Clean your digestive system
- Help flush toxins from your body
- Clean and detox your liver
- Relieve heartburn, bloating and belching
- Control constipation and diarrhoea
- Strengthen your teeth, bones and gums
- Reduce stress and fatigue
- Supply a powerful instant dose of vitamin C
- Treat nosebleeds
- Help maintain a healthy heart
- Treat colds, rheumatism, sore throat and headaches

Lemons can even make you look good! Many experts believe that the humble lemon can:

- Enhance the beauty, glow and elasticity of your skin
- Keep your hands smooth
- Help your body to grow collagen
- Quickly remove stains from your hands
- Instantly lower your stress levels
- Keep your scalp healthy and your hair from falling out
- Be a remedy for dandruff
- Reduce water retention and cellulite
- Bleach your hands and nails

After months of painstaking research, I believe I've put together a truly unique collection of secrets, tips, facts and remedies. They include innovative ways to feel healthier, prevent illness, clean your home, and look great. All for a matter of pennies.

I've also included this...

A FREE bonus report on ginger

As a little extra for you, I've also included a FREE special report on another of nature's powerful weapons: ginger. As you'll see, ginger is another must-have for your medicine cabinet.

Ginger can shift a hangover, thin the blood, freshen your breath, treat travel and morning sickness, among many other amazing qualities. Again, you'll be astounded at just how many uses ginger has. It's not just something that flavours cakes and biscuits!

Finally, a tip on how to use this book

In my view, there are two ways you can read this book.

The first way is to browse through it, put it on your shelf and refer to it whenever you think you have an everyday problem. It's okay to do this. I don't mind. I've got a full and detailed contents page so you can quickly find the right section. I've laid it out so that you can run your eyes down the page easily to spot the tips and ideas you need.

Great. But I suggest this way instead.

Find an hour of your day to spare, away from the hustle and bustle of daily life. Make a cup of tea (lemon or ginger tea!), sit in a comfy spot in a quiet room, and indulge yourself. I've written this to be an enjoyable and amusing journey into a healthier, more natural, and less expensive world.

I hope you enjoy it!

Ray Collins
The Good Life Letter
www.goodlifeletter.co.uk

CHAPTER ONE

How Lemons Became the World's Most Potent "SuperFood"

In my opinion, the best place to start something is from the beginning. For lemons, the beginning was approximately 2,500 years ago in tropical Asia, where they were first cultivated.

From there, they began a slow migration west, through northern Burma to China, across Persia and the Arab world to the Mediterranean. These early forms of lemon were probably very different to today. Smaller, with thick rinds. And not quite a "cure-all" yet. Not by a long shot.

To early Christians, the lemon was known more as a symbol of fidelity in love. In a painting called "The Virgin and Child, Saint John the Baptist, and an Angel", Jesus is seen being offered a lemon. This wasn't for any health or sanitary purposes. At that time, in dietary terms, the lemon was not hugely popular. Some very weird superstitions and prejudices surrounded them. It was thought that lemons shouldn't be given to the elderly, small children, or new mothers. In fact, lemons weren't considered a 'Super Food' but a "forbidden food". Yes, lemons were fruits that could have ill effects on the morality and physical well-being of impressionable youths.

A bit like video games or the internet today, I suppose. You can imagine parents at the time thinking: "These kids today, they don't know they're born. All they want to do is hang around the house and suck lemons."

Think what would have happened if our ancient relatives knew how amazingly powerful lemons were as a medicine at that time! How many lives would have been spared? How many diseases avoided? How many sick children brought back to health?

They could have prevented many illnesses if they'd known about vitamin C

But unfortunately not. The general ignorance continued for some years, as does our knowledge of exactly what happened next. Which is not surprising. It's not as if someone with a clipboard would begin noting the date and time the lemon first crossed each border, or cropped up in each new society.

There were bigger themes to write about, like religious wars, new empires and controversial scientific theories of stars and planets. So little is known of what happened to my favourite fruit in that time.

Even now, there is an academic argument raging about whether the ancient Romans grew and used lemons. Some say they did, others say it was a citrus fruit that artists saw on their travels and then painted on to Roman mosaics in Carthage and Pompeii. Perhaps the Romans were too busy drinking wine and nailing people to trees to bother with all that.

So let's leap to the 14th century, where the personal physician to the great Muslim leader Saladin, wrote gushingly about the lemon. And where Egyptians first invented lemonade, shortly before Christopher Columbus took the seeds of lemons with him to America, and Spanish adventurers introduced it to the New World.

Eventually the whole world woke up to the awesome potential of this fruit

Lemons became a highly valued medicine, and the subject of dozens of olde-worlde studies. In the 1600s people realised that a daily intake of lemon juice would prevent outbreaks of scurvy among sailors on long sea voyages. Symptoms of scurvy included black and blue spots, depression, exhaustion, bleeding gums, immobility and thinning hair, so it's amazing that something so simple as a lemon could help treat these nasty problems. This made it important for exploration, war, and all kinds of lucrative foreign enterprises.

This protection became crucial for the national interest; a law was passed forcing English ships to carry enough lemon juice for each sailor to get one ounce daily.

By 1636, lemons appeared in Dutch still-life paintings. But that's because they were a luxury, and only found on the table of sailors and rich folk. But by the late 19th century varieties of lemon had been developed that could be grown commercially in large quantities, especially in the US.

Which brings us to the here and now...

Lemons are now grown in Mediterranean and subtropical climates worldwide. California and Arizona are the major lemon producers, making the US a leading source ahead of Mexico and Italy. The modern lemon tree is an evergreen that grows to over six metres in height, with toothed, light green leaves. The lemons themselves are greenish to yellow in colour.

Unlike other citrus varieties, the lemon tree bears fruit continuously. What a bonus! This is like having a natural yearlong dispensary of a natural health supplement. No wonder they're so popular, and used so widely.

Today we know why they became so important after medieval times. It's now known that lemons are a powerful source of vitamin C. They are high in potassium and vitamin B1. They are classified as an "acid fruit", along with other fruits like cranberries, pineapples and strawberries. They contain 5 to 6% citric acid. Compare that with oranges, which contain only about 1%.

Because of their strong flavour, lemons are a common and versatile ingredient in many foods. They can be used to make drinks, dressings, desserts and sauces. Not only that, they can be used to soften water, clean your hair, and disinfect surfaces!

Then you have all the health benefits...

As you'll discover, lemons can get rid of toxins in the body, they can thin the blood, treat colds and coughs, fevers and flu. And as you're about to see, experts believe that they could help prevent the onset of many diseases.

Is there anything lemons *can't* do?

Well, yes. I'll admit that lemons can't do everything.

You can't heal a broken leg with a lemon. You can't launch a space shuttle on a rocket filled only with lemon juice. Not yet, anyway. You can't calm down an angry monkey by waving a lemon at it. And you can't use lemons to mop baby sick off an antique rug in bright sunlight. To be frank, you'll probably bleach it.

If you come across any book that tries to convince you that lemons are able to do any of the above, please ignore it.

Now, onwards and upwards!

CHAPTER TWO

How to Pick, Store and Use the Perfect Lemon

Having bought this book, I recognise that you're a clever, worldly person, of remarkable attractiveness. So I don't really need to tell you where to look for lemons. Unless you're reading this in California, they're probably not on the nearest tree. Shops are where I get mine. I guess you're the same.

But I will offer you some basic advice on picking, storing and using lemons. That's because when I started looking into this subject, I realised there were some great tips that I'd never heard of before. And they really work.

Here they are in full:

• Every time you're in the shop, make sure you pick up each lemon and give it a feel. The shopkeeper won't bite.

• Go for lemons with the smoothest skin and the smallest points on each end. The smoother the skin, the thinner it usually is, meaning more flesh. These will give you more juice and a better flavour.

- A good lemon should have an oily, fine texture.

- Remember that size isn't everything. A large lemon usually means it has a thick skin, which means less juice. Better to pick one that is heavy for its size. This also means it should have more juice. A lemon that looks small but feels heavier than others is the best one to pick.

- Another sign of a good lemon is a deep yellow colour. They should be firm when you touch them, but not too hard. If they are shrivelled, very hard skinned, or spongy, don't buy them.

- Avoid lemons with bruises or other signs of damage. This makes them more likely to mould. Check for any discoloration at the end of the lemon.

- Pick organic unwaxed lemons if you can, especially if you plan to use the peels, because the peel is the thing that gets it in the neck when pesticides are used. If you can't find organic, make sure you wash the lemon first.

Once you've picked the perfect lemon, you want to make sure that you store it properly. Keep them in a cool, dark place. A chilly room, cupboard or fridge will do. It should last you a couple of weeks.

However, while refrigerated lemons will last longer, you should get them out of the fridge a good while before you squeeze them. This is because room-temperature lemons will give you more juice than those from the fridge.

Here are some more easy ways to get the most out of a lemon and make it go even further, for longer...

Five tips for using lemons

In my younger years, I was the typical irresponsible, wasteful young geezer you see staggering out of pubs and into kebab shops. In those bad old days I didn't care about wasting money or useful resources. I used to cut up a whole lemon, even if I only needed a quick squeeze for a gin and tonic.

Then I discovered this little tip, and my life changed. (Well, the part of my life that involves lemons. The rest of my growing up involved reading books, paying taxes and starting a family.)

Here is the life-changing tip:

• If you only need a few drops of lemon juice, pierce one end with a fork and control the amount you squeeze out. Once done, cover the holes with cling film, and stick it in the fridge. This will keep it fresh and reusable.

And there's more...

• When you've finished with the juice/flesh of your lemon, cut the rinds off and freeze them. When you need to add zest to a recipe or a drink, just get some out, defrost and grate. It'll save you using up a fresh lemon.

• To get more juice for your money, microwave the lemon for 5-10 seconds before you juice it. Be careful not to overcook as you'll boil the juice and ruin it.

• Use the palm of your hand to roll the lemon around on a hard surface a few times before juicing. This should also bring more juice out of the fruit.

If you think these tips are good, I'm just getting warmed up. In the next chapter I've gathered together a ridiculous amounts of extraordinary health tips that involve lemons. More than you could shake the proverbial stick at.

Let's roll...

CHAPTER THREE

How Lemons Can Help
You Live a Healthier Life

If the idea of eating lemons to protect your health leaves a nasty taste in your mouth, don't panic. I'm not going to start ANY sentence with "simply eat 10 whole lemons a day". Obviously this would be impractical, expensive and you'd spend your entire life walking around with a puckered face and watering eyes.

Instead, I'm simply going to list, in alphabetical order, the ailments that lemons have been said to tackle or prevent. Where necessary, I'll tell you how much to take, and how often to take it. And I promise I'll try and make it as easy and palatable as possible.

Please let me remind you that if you are worried about a serious health condition, see a health professional and ask for medical advice. This is for your information only. And always ask your doctor before you undertake drastic dietary changes.

Got that? Great, then on with the show...

Ageing

Okay, so you can't stop the hands of time. But if you're an older person, you could find great benefits from upping your intake of vitamin C, especially if you want to keep your skin and muscles young. Lemon is packed with the stuff. Vitamin C helps the body make collagen, which is found in your ligaments, joints, bones and blood vessels. By upping your intake you will have more elasticity and strength in your body tissues.

Lemons can also ease digestive pains and other problems associated with old age. There's no one magic bullet for this. However old you are now, begin a programme of adding fresh fruit and vegetables to your diet. The following tips will reveal dozens of ways you can get lemons into your diet easily – even if you hate the stuff!

Appetite loss

Try sipping a little diluted lemon juice before and during your meal to stimulate your appetite.

Arthritis

Arthritis is a serious condition and you should speak to your doctor. But one alternative remedy that may help ease some of the suffering does involve lemon. This is because the fragrant oils found in lemon peel helps relax blood vessels and produces the effect of an anti-inflammatory.

Just take a lemon, grate the peel, and rub over the aching joint. Grate the yellow layer of lemon peel only and avoid the white pith. Once you've treated the joint, wrap the area with a cotton bandage, and leave it for two hours.

Drinking lemon juice squeezed and stirred into warm water can also relieve painful joints.

Asthma

To ease the symptoms of asthma there are two different remedies that you can try. The first is to prepare a strong drink of lemon and boiling water, add a teaspoon of honey, and drink while inhaling the steam! Another tip for this is to take half a spoonful of lemon juice before each meal, and just before you go to bed.

Or, according to Dian Dincin Buchman, author of *The Complete Book of Water Healing*, you can try a much more obscure method. You should "drink hot water and lemon juice each morning, inhaling the steam, then step into a shower and use tepid, fan shower sprays directed to the areas below the ribs, to the pit of the stomach (midline), to the midline of the back, and the sides of the chest."

Crazy, but it might just work...

Bad breath

Lemon acts as an antiseptic. So make an impromptu mouthwash using naturally squeezed lemon juice and then gargle it straight from the bottle. Rinse, then swallow. The citric acid in the juice will alter the pH level in your mouth, killing the bacteria that cause bad breath. Make sure you rinse after a few minutes, as long-term exposure to the acids in lemons can harm your tooth enamel.

Bleeding

Because of it's styptic property (meaning that it's a substance that stops external bleeding) it is said that lemons can be applied to cuts. It's also a natural antiseptic so the slight sting will do you good!

This goes for your mouth as well. Some experts have claimed that 2g of garlic and a medium-sized lemon a day pushes up the level of vitamin C in the body and stops bleeding in gums. The study, was conducted by a team of researches of the Department of Physiotherapy and Sports Science at Punjabi University.

You can also try swilling your mouth with warm honey, lemon and water (use lemon, a cup of water and 1 teaspoon of honey.)

Cancer

No, there's no cure for cancer. Neither will I pretend you can prevent the onset of cancer with a lemon. It's a superfood, but not a miracle worker. That said, lemons are packed with vitamin C, which strengthens your immune system and protects your cells from free radicals. Make that life-changing decision to add fresh fruit and vegetables – especially in their raw, organic form - to your daily diet. Get a juicer and add fresh lemon juice to your morning routine.

Cellulite

Lemon juice is good for a load of skin ailments. It can even prevent water retention. So if you suffer from cellulite you should massage some lemon oil onto the affected part of your body. Although, in my view, as we get older we should proudly let it all hang out, and give a two-fingered salute to the ageist body fascists!

Children's health

During weaning, if you add small amounts of lemon juice to baby food, it can boost a child's immune system. As the tot grows, increase the dosage slightly. You can also apply a tiny bit of lemon juice to babies' gums to relieve the pain of teething. Or you can wean your child off his or her dummy by dipping it in undiluted lemon juice.

Circulation

Lemons contain vitamin P in both its juice and its peel. This is essential for keeping your blood capillaries strong and controlling haemorrhage. In fact, it's pretty good for strengthening your whole arterial system.

Colds

The lemon has 80% of the daily recommendation of vitamin C. This boosts your immune system to fight colds. Lemon juice also lowers the toxicity of the virus so it shouldn't last as long. (See FEVER on page 28 for the classic honey, lemon and water remedy.)

Or try this: roast some lemons until they split open. Drink the juice with brown sugar and fresh pineapple juice. This should help dissolve the mucus in the throat.

Concentration

Scientists in Japan have found that lemon oil can boost your concentration. Get hold of some lemon essential oil, burn it and see for yourself if it helps when you're studying, preparing for an interview or doing the crossword.

Constipation

Squeeze a whole lemon into a mug of hot water and drink a half-hour before breakfast. Don't drink anything else for at least half an hour. Then take it at night before you go to sleep.

Corns

Apply lemon juice to your corns three times a day. At night, before you go to bed, apply the rind of the lemon with a binding or plaster to cover it and hold it against the skin overnight. Sounds mad, but you should see some surprising results.

Coughs

Here's a little homemade remedy I found. Take four tablespoons of lemon juice and 12 tablespoons of honey. Add this to six tablespoons of olive oil. Heat this mixture for five minutes, then stir for another three minutes. Cool, then take a teaspoon every couple of hours for a period of no more than 48 hours.

Cuts and bruises

Lemon is nature's antiseptic. With the juice you can disinfect minor wounds or lesions in the mouth and throat. This includes ulcers, too (see mouth ulcers on page 32). Just rub a little juice or peel over small wounds, or gargle a few times a day to kill off germs and soothe inflammation.

Dandruff

A common problem this, and apparently lemons really can do the trick. All you do is massage two tablespoons of lemon juice into your scalp and rinse with water. Then stir one teaspoon of lemon juice into one cup of water and rinse your hair with it. Shampoo afterwards, wash it again and apply lemon juice to remove the soap from your hair and scalp.

Digestion

When the liver, gall bladder and pancreas are not working properly, you can't digest your food in the right way. This can lead to constipation. Lemons are filled with minerals, especially potassium, vitamin C and bioflavonoids. They have a cleansing action on your entire body. Taking lemon juice in hot water (with honey to sweeten if you like) every morning on an empty stomach will keep your digestive system ticking over.

Ears

Squeeze out 200g of lemon juice and 50mgs of mustard oil. Heat them in a bowl until there's only oil left. Put this in a small bottle and keep in the fridge. Put a couple of drops in your ear to ease pain.

Eyes

If you've got sore eyes from smoke, pollution or a heavy night's driving, then it might surprise you to know that lemon can help here, too! You take one drop of lemon juice and add it to 28ml of warm water. Now use it like a regular eyewash solution you'd buy in the shops.

Fever

The lemon is a classic remedy for people with a fever associated with colds and flu. The best way I've found is to mix the juice of a lemon with boiling water and two teaspoons of honey. I didn't need to research this one, it's a remedy that my family have used as long as I can remember.

Gallstones

Many naturopaths believe that if you suffer from gallstones, lemon juice can help. Gallstones occure when your body tries to destroy a bacteria by calcifying the bile surrounding it. Obviously, it's something your should talk to your doctor about, as they can be painful, difficult to remove, and can even cause further infection.

Some say lemons can help this. For instance one weird and slightly hardcore recipe I found (this is repeated on many naturopath websites) says that " if the stones are small enough, they can be flushed by taking 300mls of olive oil and the juice of two lemons at 8am, repeating at 9am and 10am, then at 1pm, taking two teaspoonfuls (10ml) of Epsom salts in a glass of warm water."

Interesting information, but personally, I'd talk to a medical professional before administering this kind of thing. It sounds, as my son would say, "minging".

Gout

This happens when you get too much uric acid in your blood and tissues, which then crystallizes in the joints. Lemon juice prevents this by helping your body form calcium carbonate, which neutralizes the acids in the body. This includes the uric acid that causes those attacks of gout. After each meal you should drink the juice of one lemon in a mug of lukewarm water.

Greasy hair

Lemons can regulate the sebaceous glands in your head, to prevent them producing too much oil. The juice of two lemons mixed with a pint of distilled water makes a great rinse and will help reduce the oil on your scalp. (Unless you want an 80s era George Michael or Bros look, don't do this in the sun! You'll be blonde!)

Gum disease

Chewing the skin of lemons is a novel way to strengthen your gums.

Hair loss

Hair loss can happen due to many reasons such as stress, poor diet, hormone imbalance, lack of rest and poor hair care. If any of these are relevant to you, then make sure you explore these avenues first. But once you've exhausted these, there may be a way to prevent hair loss with lemon.

A basic idea is to try mixing lemon juice with shampoo to act as a hair tonic. Or try this recipe:

Take two eggs, one tablespoon of ground almond, one teaspoon curry powder, one tablespoon of lemon juice, one glass of fresh orange juice, one tablespoon of crushed coriander leaves and a pinch of black pepper. Mix together and leave for one hour. Apply it, keep it on for an hour, wash off shampoo, then repeat three times each week.

You can imagine the telly advert...

"Take two bottles into the shower?"

"No thanks, I've got a lemon."

Hangovers

For the headache side of things, see HEADACHE on page 31. But here's what some public speakers and businessmen have done when they need to speak the morning after big nights on the tiles. To re-invigorate yourself, you cut a lemon into quarters, sprinkle it with salt, then eat the flesh (not the rind) before breakfast. Apparently this is an effective stimulant!

Or you can get really strange with this one, if you don't mind looking like a wally. And let's admit it, when you've got a stinking hangover you'll try anything if you think it might work, even a teensy-weensy bit. And if it helps, people apparently do this in Puerto Rico.

What you do is get some lemon slices and rub them under your armpits. The idea is that lemon juice helps you keep in fluid and stops dehydration. Well? Over to you!

A sensible thing to do to prevent hangovers is drink a glass of water with lemon juice in it before going to bed. The water will reduce dehydration and lemon is packed with Vitamin C, which breaks down alchol in your liver. The lemon will help relieve your thirst and boost you vitamin C levels to help you cope with the next day.

Headache

There are loads of old wives tales' and tips around on this subject. One New York barman cures hangover headaches by adding three teaspoons of lemon juice to hot tea. Another way I've heard to help relieve a throbbing headache is to rub a slice of lemon against your temples and forehead. Here's another one for good measure: drink a mixture of half a cup of strong black coffee with the juice of half a lemon.

Hyperacidity

Here's a surprising one. Lemon juice can actually reduce acidity in the stomach. It creates a barrier in the body that stops acidity reaching the gut.

Insomnia

Lemon tea helps the body relax and the mind settle down, and can aid a deep, restful sleep. Drink a cup of lemon tea before settling down for the night.

Kidney stones

Lemon juice acts as a powerful diuretic. In layman's terms, this means that it helps you wee more. It also contains citric acid, which acts on the liver to build up its enzymes. This helps it remove toxins in the blood. It also combines with calcium to form soluble chemical substances which can help remove kidney and pancreatic stones.

Mouth ulcers

Squeeze the juice of a lemon into a glass, mix with an equal amount of water, close your eyes and gargle in your mouth. Okay, so this may seem a crazy move because it stings. But be brave. This will disinfect the ulcers and kill any bacteria. Or if you're feeling especially heroic, dab pure lemon juice directly on the ulcers with a cotton bud. It burns, but works.

Nightmares

Here's an old wives' take that just might work. Certainly no harm in giving it a try and, besides, if it does nothing else it will help with treating rough skin on your feet. What you do is soak your feet in warm water for 10 minutes. Then rub them with half a lemon. Don't rinse them off, just pat them dry. Now go back to bed. Maybe you'll have pleasant dreams of lovely lemons... or nightmares of huge angry lemons chasing you through a shopping centre.

Nosebleeds

Dip a cotton bud into some diluted lemon juice and dab the inside of your nostril. This will help seal the small broken vessels by tightening the delicate nasal membrane.

Piles

Not to be laughed at, this is a painful and embarrassing condition. Lemons to the rescue? Well, perhaps. Try adding some lemon juice to water and drinking it every day before you go to the toilet. That's the easy bit...

Now, when you go to bed, mix half a tablespoon of lemon juice with half a spoon of glycerine. (Have a look for this online, or in any local chemist. it's widely available and easy to find.) Dab this mixture against the anus, cover with a cloth and go to sleep if you can. It's said to do the trick.

Poison ivy rash

If you get a poison ivy rash, you don't necessarily need to slather yourself in tonnes of calamine lotion. Apply lemon juice directly to the affected area to soothe the itching and reduce the rash.

Preventing illness

If you're prone to – or worried about – getting infections, fevers and illnesses of the stomach, liver and intestines, then lemon is a powerful preventative. Simply up your intake of fresh lemon juice every day. It will keep your immune system primed and your health in tip-top condition.

Prickly heat

For some relief, knock back three drinks of cool, freshly-squeezed lemon juice throughout the day.

Relaxation

There's nothing like a soothing cleansing bath to relax in, is there? So take two bags of lemon tea, add them to 225ml of hot water, add a cup of milk and three teaspoons of fresh lemon juice. Basically, make a cup of tea, remove the bags, stir it up and add it to your bath water. Get in and add the hot water until it's as hot as you can take, then relax for half an hour.

Rough skin

If you have rough hands or sore feet, rinse them in a mixture of equal parts lemon juice and water, then massage with olive oil and dab dry with a soft cloth.

Scaly elbows

If your elbows get dry and itchy, it's annoying and uncomfortable. Even worse, they look terrible too, especially in hot weather when you go out in T-shirts. But never fear, your elbows will look and feel better if you mix baking soda and lemon juice into a rough paste. Now rub the paste into your elbows. This makes for a soothing smoothing, and exfoliating treatment. Try it once a day until the symptoms disappear.

Skin cleanser

Lemon juice can help your body cleanse itself. It does so by raising the body temperature very, very slightly. This causes perspiration, which flushes toxins out of your skin. Or you can add lemon rind or lemon juice to your bath. This can help soothe you. If you've been out in the sun too long, mix three drops of lemon juice with water and put it into a spray bottle. Give yourself a squirt and relax.

Sore throat

Squeeze one lemon and mix the juice with one cup of hot water. Gargle three times a day. This works for hoarseness, too.

Stings

Dab some pure lemon juice on those pesky wasp and bee stings to relieve the pain and inflammation.

Stress and fatigue

When you have a stress disorder you should up your intake of vitamin C. Immediately begin taking lemon and water every morning, and eating plenty of other fresh fruit and vegetables.

Sunburn

Mix one part lemon juice with three parts water and apply this to the affected area. The juice acts as an astringent. This calms the skin down.

Tired feet

You've come in from a hard day's walking, standing, shopping, or whatever it is that makes them pound and ache at the end of the day. What you should do now is soak them in a bowl of hot water and rub them with lemon juice.

Vaginal itching

If you suffer itching after intercourse, wrap a bit of paper towel, or thin cloth around a finger. Dip this into a solution made up of a tablespoon of lemon juice and half a cup of water. Insert your wrapped finger into the vagina and wipe the inside with a circular motion.

Warts

If you've tried countless remedies to get rid of your warts, and nothing seems to work, here's a tip: rub some lemon juice directly to the wart with a cotton swab. If you do this for several days the acids in the lemon juice can begin to dissolve the wart.

CHAPTER FOUR

Why Everyone Should Keep a Lemon in their Bathroom Cabinet

"So Ray, how do you keep your skin so soft and young-looking...?"

Allright, all right. Nobody asks me that question. I can't even add the words "any more", because even as a baby I always looked less like a little angel and more like a little Sid James.

So the beauty industry is something that's gone completely over my head. Of course, my wife Lara knows every last thing about exfoliators, moisturisers, skin polishers and pore cleansers. In fact, when we first met she could spend a whole day cooing with girlfriends over a tiny bottle of lotion, insisting it would change her life forever.

But the thing is (as Lara and I discovered the more we looked into natural remedies and treatments) you really don't have to spend a fortune on beauty products. Really, most of the stuff you buy in shops is designed to make the manufacturers rich, not make you young.

Yet people are so desperate for the "next big thing", they'll pretty much try anything to beat age...

And I mean ANYTHING...

How the cosmetics industry is making a fortune from our insecurities

The anti-ageing market is big business, and people will try almost anything (and pay almost anything) to look younger. But you'd think they'd draw the line at poo, wouldn't you?

Well, not the ladies of Knightsbridge, oh no. In order to beat ageing, these ladies who lunch are queuing up to try the latest miracle wrinkle cure – nightingale poo.

I swear this is true.

The poo is applied to the face for 90 minutes, and the salons claim the results have been unbelievable. Apparently, this remedy was first introduced by the geisha girls of Kyoto. They used a compound made from nightingale droppings to remove make-up and keep their skin smooth and youthful.

Of course, the droppings aren't just taken from the bird and slapped directly onto your face. They are mixed with white clay, which is then treated to remove all bacteria before being applied as a mask.

But even so, it all seems a bit extreme. (Although not as extreme as one hair treatment currently on offer... a shampoo made from bull semen) It's certainly not something I fancy trying, but it seems people with money are more than happy to slap anything on their face.

Hey. Maybe I've hit upon a great little home business idea for all you budgie or parrot owners.

When you clean out the cage, bottle up all the droppings and smack a fancy label on it (maybe something in French. Le Crap perhaps?). Now you can start a mail order business.

In the meantime, here are some great natural skin treatments that don't involve you having to go round your neighbourhood scraping muck off car windows. In fact, as you're about to discover, our friend the lemon pretty much covers ALL of your skin care needs...

How lemons can make your skin look healthier, fresher and make you feel GREAT!

Now I'm not going to pretend the humble lemon can take 20 years off your looks, or turn you from Wayne Rooney to George Clooney, no siree.

But if you don't fancy sneaking up behind a nightingale, bursting a crisp packet just behind it's back and scooping up the results, and you don't want to spend ridiculous sums of money on fancy skin care products... then listen up. There are dozens of ways that lemons can leave your skin feeling fresh and looking great.

Now this section isn't in alphabetical order. Otherwise it would read 'skincare, skincare, skincare again.

But to try and give it some structure so you can quickly find what you want, I've split it up into sections: Anti-ageing, Beauty and Cleansing, (that covers anything I can't fit into the first three sections).

Before we get going...

A few words of warning

Although lemon juice is (of course) 100% natural, it can still cause skin sensitivity or irritation. After all, it's pretty acidic stuff. So always test any of the following treatments on a small area of skin first to see how you react.

And a second warning: Avoid going out in the sun for at least 12 hours after using any of these lemon skin treatments. Lemon juice is photo toxic, which means it reacts to the UV rays in sunlight. This reaction can cause burns, blisters or brown patches – the very things we're trying to get rid of! So play it smart, and follow these two rules.

Okay, that's enough of me wagging a finger at you...

Let's look at the treatments!

ANTI-AGING

Hide the evidence! How to get rid of age spots with lemon juice

Age spots (or liver spots) are one of the biggest tell-tale signs that age is creeping up on you and you're now officially the oldest teenager in town. Right?

Well, surprisingly this is wrong. Age spots have little to do with age itself, and all to do with the effects of the sun on your skin. Of course, the more years you spend on the planet, the more time you'll be exposed to sunshine, so you could argue it IS a sign of age. But the truth is, it's all down to sunny days lazing around on the beach. In fact, even a little bit of sun worshipping can cause age spots later in life.

So what actually causes the spots?

As we all know, sunshine contains ultraviolet rays, which cause the skin to tan and/or burn. But each time the skin changes colour, more and more pigment gets left in the skin, until eventually, the pigment doesn't fade away. Instead, it forms brown skin lesions known as age spots (aka liver spots or sun spots).

There are a few ways to get those tell-tale age spots to fade away. For example, you'll find numerous over-the-counter, skin-bleaching creams containing a "magic" ingredient called hydroquinone, a man-made drug that blocks the colouring process.

But, as with so many synthetic drugs, there can be complications... Blisters, swelling, a gradual blue-black darkening of the skin (ochronosis), itching, severe swelling, dizziness and trouble breathing. The recorded side effects aren't nice at all.

Of course, it's very unlikely any of these symptoms will affect you. Chances are you could take drugs like hydroquinone happily ever after without anything happening (although ALWAYS follow the instructions on the packet. Better still, check things out with your doctor BEFORE you start taking drugs, even over-the-counter ones).

In my humble opinion, it's not worth the risk. Especially when lemon juice can tackle the problem efficiently and safely.

Here are four remedies for you to try:

- **Pure and simple:** Just dab lemon juice onto them and leave them alone for 15 minutes. After that, rinse your skin clean. Repeat as often as you like (but don't go crazy, once a day should do it) until the spots begin to fade.

- **The cake mix:** Mix together an egg white, a tablespoon of fine sugar, a tablespoon of lemon juice, and a tablespoon of hydrogen peroxide.Make sure you get 3% peroxide from your chemist and talk to them first. You need the stuff you can safely bathe in, or splash on your skin. Dab the mixture onto the spots, let it dry out, and then wash it off (unless you want to be attacked by wasps in the summer!).

- **Heavy duty treatment.** Do the same as above, but leave out the hydrogen peroxide, and replace with an extra tablespoon of lemon juice. Beat the mixture until it becomes thick and massage it into your skin before you go to bed. Leave it to work its magic overnight, then wash off in the morning.

- **The Mediterranean remedy:** Mix three parts lemon juice to one part olive oil and pat onto any sun-darkened areas or age spots. Repeat every day until they fade.

Cleopatra's anti-wrinkle treatment

I've seen this recipe written up in quite a few places as Cleopatra's anti-wrinkle treatment, which always strikes me as odd. I mean, surely the ruler of one of the most powerful and advanced civilisations on earth had more pressing matters to attend to than write a book of beauty treatments?

I'm not saying she didn't use natural remedies, and by all accounts she was beautiful, but I somehow can't quite picture her sitting at her desk writing *The Must-Have Beauty Treatments for the Modern 2000BC Girl* – feeding parchment into a typewriter, and bashing away at dozens of hieroglyphic keys.

Still, I suppose someone had to call this skin-care recipe something, and I'm guessing the *Pat Butcher Anti-Wrinkle Treatment* wouldn't have gone down half as well.

Here's what you need:

Two unpeeled cucumbers, whipped cream, a tablespoon of olive oil, a tablespoon of honey, a little cornstarch and several halved lemons.

Slice the cucumbers into the smallest strips or cubes you can without leaving your fingertips on the chopping board. Put them into the blender, and add dollops of whipping cream bit by bit until the mixture makes a nice paste. Then add the olive oil and honey and give it a quick whiz until it disappears.

Add a large pinch of cornstarch, blend for a few more seconds, then leave it in the fridge for at least half an hour.

When you're ready to apply the mixture, quickly and lightly rub your face and neck with the lemon halves, but don't wipe your face dry. Beware that lemon is very acidic and will react on the skin if you scrub it to hard.

Lie in a reclining position and apply the cucumber-cream mixture. Better still, get someone to put it on for you, otherwise you'll probably end up with half your face covered and half bare. (Or, knowing me, I'd absentmindedly think "hmmm, tasty" and spoon it into my mouth Homer Simpson style.)

Leave the mask on for between an hour, and an hour and a half, before removing.

Once you've cleaned your face up, dip your fingers into some more whipped cream and massage it in. Let it dry naturally, then wash off with nothing but water.

Crikey. Cleopatra had a bit of spare time on her hands, didn't she? But if you can spare the time, give this a try. My human guineapig Lara says it works wonders.

BEAUTY

Want the Paris Hilton look?

Well you don't have to walk around with a tiny dog and get thrown in jail for that.

Just mix $\frac{1}{4}$ cup lemon juice with $\frac{3}{4}$ cup water (if you're reading this, Paris, they're fractions) and rinse your hair with it. Then sit in the sun until your hair dries, and the natural bleaching agents in the lemon juice will lighten your hair. Depending on how light you want to go, do this daily for up to a week.

The lemon manicure

Add the juice of $\frac{1}{2}$ a lemon to one cup of warm water and soak your fingertips in the mixture for five minutes. Once the cuticles are soft, push them back and rub some of the peel over the nail for a while to buff them up.

Sore hands

Lemon juice is an excellent way to relieve sore hands. Simply rub with the juice, rinse off, then massage your hands with olive oil or coconut oil.

Anti-stress treatment

Soak a small towel in warm water and squeeze it dry. Place fresh lemon slices in the centre of the towel and roll it up. Microwave for 30 seconds, drape it over the back of your neck, close your eyes and lie back on a comfy chair. Try counting to 60, and see how far you get before everything just seems to drift away.

The best friend a girl can have!

This could really go in the "cleansing" section. In fact, it should go in the cleansing section, but this seems to be such an important part of a girl's daily beauty routine I put it here instead, because this is THE ultimate cleanser.

It will remove excess oil, tighten your skin and deep-clean your pores so that every last trace of make-up and dirt that can clog your pores is lifted away.

After you've cooked with lemons, squeeze the last remnants of juice into a cup, dilute with twice the amount of water, and store it in an airtight bottle in the fridge.

Next day the mixture is ready to use. Simply clean your face as per usual, then apply this to your face with a cotton ball. Keep the mixture in the fridge when not in use. This is the BEST astringent you'll ever have.

Foot soak

I don't suppose I'll ever get a job as a filing clerk, because I'm not sure if this is in the right section either. After all, it's not often you get your feet wolf-whistled at.

But this feels so good, I'm happy to class it as a beauty treatment.

First, prepare your foot spa. Take half a lemon and dip it into some granulated sugar. Set it to one side and soak your feet in hot water for 10-15 minutes, before massaging your feet with the sugary lemon in slow circular motions.

Now rinse your feet with cool water and pat them dry. They should feel cool and ache-free.

CLEANSING

Deep cleansing

This is one where you should really keep your eyes closed! To deep-clean your face and remove all the grime and pollution that's clogged up your pores during the day, squeeze the juice of half a lemon into a bowl, dip your fingertips in and massage your skin in small circular movements. If you have any blackheads that need weeding out, make sure you dab them individually with the juice. This will help draw them out. After a few days of doing this, your skin should look much, much healthier.

The lemon rind cleanser

Take a few rinds of lemon, mix with equal parts of water and olive oil, and heat for a few minutes until everything warms through. While the mixture is still warm, paint it on your face and neck with a pastry brush. When it is thoroughly dry, wash it off with warm water and pat dry.

Zit zapper

Let's face it, spots have a nasty habit of making a guest appearance when you least want them. On the eve of a job interview, or just before you're due to go out on a date, a spot will suddenly appear like a red traffic light smack bang in the middle of your face.

Most creams won't act quickly enough to get rid of the offending sight in time for your big day, but a lemon might just do the trick...

Simply mix equal measures of lemon juice, apple cider vinegar and salt, and mix it into a paste. Dab it onto the spot and leave it overnight. The mixture will dry out the infection and turn the volume down from an horrific 10 to a barely noticeable one or two.

Even if you only have a couple of hours to get rid of a spot, give this a go. It should make a big difference.

Body clean

Sorry... this sounds like part of an undertaker's job, doesn't it? But I couldn't think of a nicer way to put it. Body reviver perhaps? No, that sounds even worse, like I'm trying to raise the dead.

Let's just stick with *Body Clean*.

This treatment is a great way to gently clean all the pores of your body without having to dab every inch of your skin. (My tummy alone would take two full days!). Besides, some parts of your body are a little more sensitive than others, so we need something milder for an all over body soak. And this recipe works wonders.

Boil a kettle and pour over two bags of lemon tea. Once the tea has steeped for five minutes, pour into a bowl and add a cup of milk and three teaspoons of lemon juice. Stir well, then pour into a running bath.

Now the easy bit. Have a looooooong soak.

Beat the boils

If you suffer from boils, simply heat up a whole lemon in your oven (nothing drastic, just get it warm) then slice it in half and press the flesh against the boil. It may look silly, but secure it there with a strip of tape for an hour or so. The warm lemon juice will draw the infection to the surface, and dry it out.

Once the boil erupts, boil some water and add two tablespoons of lemon juice. Let it cool, then clean and disinfect the area with the potion. Cover with a sterile bandage. For the next few days, two to three times a day, remove the bandage and apply a warm, wet compress, leaving it on for 15 minutes. Re-dress the area with a fresh sterile bandage each time until the boil has completely healed.

CHAPTER FIVE

Lemon The Super Cleaner

In my weekly *Good Life Letters* you'll often find me championing natural remedies over man-made drugs for two very simple reasons. First off, natural remedies are unquestionably better for our bodies. I mean, you rarely hear about someone being rushed to hospital after reacting badly to a raspberry, do you?

Secondly, they are often just as powerful, sometimes even MORE powerful than man-made drugs. The problem is, they are ignored because big business can't patent a natural remedy. And what they can't patent, they can't make money out of.

And there's a third reason. Natural remedies often taste great, so it's easy to get them into your system and get them fighting on our behalf. And in all honesty, I can't say the same about man-made drugs.

I don't think I'd ever find myself rooting around in the fridge for a plate of tasty anti-inflammatory drugs, (even if they were safe) by the handful. And I've never wistfully looked out of my window wishing an E-number tree would grow in my garden.

But strawberries? Chocolate? (Ignore what health nags say; it's healthy in sensible amounts.) Roast chicken?

Bring them on! They're healthy AND there are no nasty side effects.

And although it doesn't excite me nearly as much, the same can be said for house cleaning. Big companies will spend millions creating chemical concoctions, then give them names like "Summer Meadow" and 'Dewy Forest Where Pixies Play.

Who do they think they're kidding? Not only do they smell foul (they should be called "Rotted Fruit" and "Urgggggh"), they're full of skin-irritants and poisons that you simply don't need to clean a table top!

In many household products there are nasty solvents known as Volatile Organic Compounds. They are found in paint, cleaning products, and especially air fresheners.

Many experts believe these are bad news. The University of Bristol studied 10,000 mothers and infants to look at the effects of Volatile Organic Compounds. They found that in homes where they were used daily, 32% more babies had diarrhoea and earache.... and that the mothers also had 10% more headaches and became 26% more susceptible to depression.

Another worrying fact is that over 5% of adults in the UK now have eczema, which involves red, dry, itchy skin, lumps, blisters and weeping sores. Again, many experts now believe this is partly down to our dependence on artificial cleaning agents, solvents, detergents, oils and other gunk.

The thing is, there are plenty of healthy alternatives to commercial air fresheners. They're not only natural and gunk-free, they're cheaper!

Here's where the humble lemon really comes into its own.

Chopping boards

Your poor chopping board. Just think of things you slap on it, crush on it and leak on it. Onions, garlic, fish, raw meat. It's no wonder it can start to look tired (and smell tired) after a while.

And sometimes it needs more than a clean in soapy water to revive it.

To get rid of the accumulated smell and help kill off any stubborn germs that cling on for dear life in the washing-up bowl, rub it all over with the cut side of half a lemon. Don't skimp. Give it a really good scrub. Let the juice dry, then rinse off with water.

Kitchen cabinets

To keep your cabinets clean and grease-free, just mix ¼ of a cup of juice with a mug of hot water, and wipe the surfaces down as required.

Keep the silverware shiny

To clean brass or silver, mix lemon juice and baking soda until it becomes as thick as cream cheese, then simply rub into the metal with a soft, clean cloth. Wipe clean with a separate cloth. Be sure to wash the metal afterwards in warm soapy water, as the acid in lemon may will start to attack the metal and cause pitting.

Plastic containers

To make a discoloured plastic container scrub up well, rub half a lemon over the insides, then let it sit in the sun for a day. The sun and the lemon juice will bleach out all the stains and make the container look as good as new.

Limescale

Use half a lemon to clean the limescale off a sink or tap. Rub the cut end over the crusty spot and rinse away.

Warning: don't use this on gold plated taps.

Berry stains

Who doesn't like picking berries? Well, what I really mean is who doesn't like eating them? Berry picking is one of the few things the whole family likes to do, but after all that scoffing, it can leave your hands purple. And no matter how much you scrub with soap and water, it's a stain that stubbornly refuses to shift. Instead, try washing your hands with undiluted lemon juice first. Rub your hands together thoroughly, wait a few minutes, then wash with warm, soapy water.

Air freshener

Use lemon to freshen the air by making a mixture of equal parts lemon juice and water and putting it in a spray bottle. Honestly, this is MUCH better than any artificial freshener you'll find.

Bad smelling bins

If your kitchen bin is starting to pong a bit, just stick some lemon peel in it. Likewise, if you have a waste disposal unit, toss the peel down the drain.

Bleach

Most people use basic supermarket bleach to remove stains, but there's a problem with this.

The chemicals can lift the iron content from the water and deposit them as stains in the fabric. So if you want to remove marks on clothes, try soaking them in a mixture of lemon juice and baking soda for at least half an hour before washing normally.

Sweat stains

You can remove unsightly underarm stains from shirts and blouses simply by scrubbing them with a mixture of equal parts lemon juice and water.

Powerful clothes wash

You've seen the ads. There's always some stubborn stains that ordinary powders "just can't shift". But you never see the smiling housewives reaching for a lemon, do you?

Well you should, because lemon juice has enough clout to lift stains like rust and mineral discolourations. All you have to do is pour one cup of lemon juice into the washer during the wash cycle. The natural bleaching action of the juice will zap the stains and leave the clothes smelling fresh. Lovely.

Mildew

You know how it is. You store summer clothes away for the winter thinking they're safe and sound, then when you're ready to bound out into the summer air your favourite item is stained with mildew. Then you – a grown person – start crying. All right, maybe that's only my reaction, but it hurts when your red Hawaiian parrot shirt or floaty dress isn't fit to wear.

However, with the trusty lemon by your side, there's no problem. To get rid of mildew on clothes, make a paste of lemon juice and salt and rub it on the offending area, then dry the clothes in sunlight. Repeat the process until the stain is gone.

Make your whites whiter!

Simply add some lemon juice to your wash, and the bleaching effect of the citrus will whiten your whites. Add more or less depending on how much whitening you want to do.

Window cleaning

Simply cut a lemon into quarters and rub a section over your windows, squeezing the lemon as you go. As soon as you've finished, wipe the glass with a damp cloth, then with a dry one. You honestly won't believe how clear this makes the glass.

Microwave cleaning

To clean a microwave, place half a lemon in water and cook on high for about five minutes. This loosens stubborn burnt on foods, making them easy to wipe away with a damp cloth.

Fridge odours

I don't know about you, but if I'm not careful I can leave food in the fridge so long an archaeologist might well discover it in the next century and put it in a museum. So it's always my job in the house to clean out the fridge.

Which is why I love this little tip...
To keep your fridge odour-free, cut a lemon in half and put it on a saucer right near the back of your fridge. The lemon will happily sit there and suck up any rotten smells coming from your fridge, so when you come to clean it out it won't be such a disgusting job.

Fireplace odours

Ahhh, the roar of an open fire! There's nothing quite like it when the nights are drawing in. That is, until the fire starts belching out smoky smells that fill the whole room.

If this happens to you, try throwing a few lemon peels into the flames. Or simply burn some lemon peels along with your firewood to stop it happening in the first place.

Marble stains

You'd think marble would be pretty tough wouldn't you? But in reality marble is the Graham Norton of the stone gang: glamorous with a soft centre.

You see marble isn't really a stone at all, but a fossilised form of old sea shells which can stain quite easily. The trouble is, these stains are hard to get rid of. Sometimes no amount of scrubbing can do it

So if you're struggling with stained marble, give this a go...

Cut a lemon in half, dip it into some salt, then scrub away at the stain. Rinse the residue off, and hopefully you should see the stain lifting.

But beware! You should only try this if you're at your wits end. The acid in the lemon could turn nasty and leave a mark of its own.

Air freshener

If you're like me, you'll hate the smell of synthetic air fresheners. To me it feels like you're being hugged and kissed by 100 overbearing aunts all at once.

So try this instead...
Stick an enamelled cast-iron pot or bowl on top of a wood-burning stove or hob, fill with water, and add lemon peels, cinnamon sticks, cloves, and apple skins. Just bring the water to a simmer and let the vapour drift through the house, freshening the place as it goes.

Cat litter odours

I love cats, but the smell from their litter trays? I'd rather stick my head in a bucket of bird poo. (That may sound strange if you haven't read page 38!)

But instead of going crazy with air freshening sprays, just cut a handful of lemons in half, and leave them face up on a plate in the room. The lemon flesh will soak up the smell, and replace it with the soft scent of lemon groves instead.

Aluminium

Aluminium pots and pans go dull very, very quickly, but it's easy to inject them with a fresh lease of life. Just rub the cut side of half a lemon all over them and buff up with a soft cloth.

Humidifier

If you have one of these contraptions at home, you'll know they can start smelling a bit weird after a while. To combat this, simply add three or four teaspoons of lemon juice into the water.

Chrome

If your chrome is dull, or minerals have built up over the years, just rub lemon rind over the surface and you'll get it so shiny you'll be able to see yourself in it (which maybe isn't such a good idea in my case!). Rinse well and dry with a soft cloth.

CHAPTER SIX

Lemon Lucky Dip

Here are even more uses for the mighty lemon that didn't seem to fit into any of the previous chapters. So have a read and see if there's anything else a lemon might be able to help you out with...

A brilliant party idea
Cut a lemon into slices and then cut them in half again. Put these into an ice cube tray with water. When frozen pop them into your drink. It looks great and tastes delicious.

Cleaning coins
Yes, it's strange. But I don't know... SOMEONE might want to do this. Who am I to deny them the one tip that could change their life forever?

If you want copper coins to come up looking like new, put them in a cup of lemon juice, add a pinch of salt, and let it let stand overnight.

Recharge a battery!

All you need for this is a lemon, a penny and strip of zinc. Make sure the zinc and the penny are clean by polishing them with a piece of sandpaper. Squeeze the lemon without splitting the peel to release the juices inside. Cut a pair of slits in the top of the lemon about 1-2 cm apart. Insert the penny in one slit and the zinc in the other.

Now try using small bulldog clips to recharge a battery, by attaching one set to the penny and zinc, and the other to the battery.

Prevent potatoes from turning brown

You know they're fresh, I know they're fresh. But potatoes (and cauliflower) have a nasty habit of turning brown when boiling. And this isn't a good look when you're having guests over for dinner. To prevent this happening, pop a teaspoon of fresh lemon juice into the cooking water.

Keep rice from sticking

To keep your rice from sticking together like some sticky snowball, add a spoonful of lemon juice to the boiling water when cooking. When the rice is done, let it cool for a few minutes, then fluff with a fork before serving.

Keep guacamole green

Here's another curse of the kitchen: brown guacamole. Turn your back on it for a minute and it seems to turn brown.

Here's an easy remedy. Sprinkle fresh lemon juice over it and it will stay fresh and green. Lemon juice goes well with guacamole, so there's no danger of ruining the flavour.

You can use this tip with apples, bananas, or any other fruit that does its darndest to look disgusting if it's neglected for even a minute.

Keep your juices colourful

If you own a juicer, the above tip is also useful for keeping your fresh fruit juices from going that muddy brown colour. Squeeze a drop of lemon into the mix and stir.

Crisp lettuce every time

Here's a little kitchen mystery. You buy some lettuce, use a little and put the rest away. But in what seems like a minute, the next time you open the fridge door the lettuce has gone all limp and soggy.

Rather than throw it away, you can revive it with a little lemon juice. Simply squeeze half a lemon into a bowl of cold water, stick your underperforming lettuce in it and keep it in the fridge for an hour. Then take it out, pat the leaves dry, and voila! The lettuce is as fresh as... er, a fresh lettuce!

Repel insects

Some people spend a ton of money arming themselves with all sorts of bug sprays when there's really no need. Just follow this routine and most insects will pack up and move next door...

First, squirt some lemon juice on door thresholds and windowsills. Then squeeze lemon juice into any holes or cracks where creepy crawlies can get in. Finally, scatter small slices of lemon peel around the outdoor entrance. This will block most of the ways into the house, and insects will look for easier targets, much like a burglar will avoid a house that has an alarm and a *Beware of the Dog* sticker.

Got a farm...?

Dehydrated lemon peel is used as cattle feed. I don't know what you're going to do with this tip (unless my next book is called *"How to Buy and Look After Cattle"*), but I just thought I'd throw it in for free!

Flower freshener

Apparently, if you pour a little fresh lemonade onto potted plants, it can keep their flowers fresh longer than normal. (Who discovers these things?) But it cannot be used on chrysanthemums, because their leaves will turn brown.

CHAPTER SEVEN

Lemon – The X-files Episode

Imagine a lemon sitting in a small tent at a carnival, wearing a gypsy bandanna and asking to have its palm crossed with silver so it can read your future. Sounds stupid doesn't it?

Although you might change your mind after reading this...

The strange case of the lemon and the tongue

Scientists are currently working on a theory that a drop of lemon juice on your tongue might tell you something about your personality.

How? By measuring the amount of saliva you produce. (Honestly, the things these scientists get up to. Don't they have proper jobs?)

Anyway, there's a part of your brain called the Reticular Activating System (RAS) which responds to outside influences. Food, meeting a friend, the weather, soft drinks, watching sports... almost everything can affect your RAS. And lemon juice just happens to be one of those things that gives your RAS a real kick.

You see, your RAS mechanism controls the amount of saliva you produce when your mouth comes into contact with food. The outside influence hits your body and the RAS responds. By squeezing just one drop of lemon juice on your tongue, you can produce a pretty strong reaction from your RAS. Basically, it causes your mouth to water like crazy.

So far, so what? "Lemon juice makes your mouth water" is hardly a shock headline.

Well here's the interesting bit...

Scientists now believe that introverts have more RAS activity than most. Which means a drop of lemon juice on an introvert's tongue will produce more saliva than an average person would.

However, in extroverts (or in layman's terms, the uncle that dances to Duran Duran at weddings with a tea towel wrapped around his head) there is a much lower level of activity in the RAS. They require more outside influence to get their RAS to even notice something's going on. This means that a drop of lemon juice on an extrovert's tongue would produce far less saliva.

So here's the question...

Do you want to find out what sort of personality you have? Or your family or friends?

Try this simple test and you'll soon be able to "predict" whether people are more likely to stand in the corner at parties, or flamenco dance naked with a rose between their teeth...

How to read people's personalities with a lemon

For the test you'll need:

• Lemon juice
• Kitchen scales
• Cotton wool balls

Once you've got your volunteers, you put a drop of lemon juice on your tongue and count to 10, slooshing around any liquid that builds up in your mouth.

Use the cotton wool balls to soak up all the saliva. Take your time, and try and get as much as you can. Put the cotton wool balls on your kitchen scales and see how much they weigh. Compare your results with your friends and family, and see whose weighs the most.

The people who produce more saliva (ie. whose cotton balls weigh more) are likely to be more introverted and quiet.

If you have someone whose cotton ball comes out dry – watch out! They're the ones who'll start heckling comedians from the crowd, who'll challenge a stranger to a kissing contest and who'll generally be happy to show you up.

CHAPTER EIGHT

Introducing the "Gastro Lemon"

Okay. You've seen how lemons can treat spots, re-grow hair, help ease arthritis pain, polish silver, clean windows, recharge a battery, and even tell you what personality you have.

But in all that excitement we've almost forgotten the one use for lemon that's staring us right in the face... food and drink!

Naturally, no lemon book would be complete with out covering this topic, especially as food and drink is my specialist subject. In fact, I'd make an excellent scientist if food and drink was a category worthy of study in the same way as health.

I can just see my notes now...

"In a study of one, results suggest that eating a large, rare steak with chips and peppercorn sauce, followed by apple pie has a 93% success rate of causing sleep in front of the omnibus edition of *EastEnders*."

Unfortunately, there doesn't seem to be much call for this kind of dedicated scientist, so I guess I'll just have to carry on with the day job.

To kick this section off, let's have a look at a few simple tricks that a lemon can help you with in the kitchen...

Tough meat
If you want to avoid tough, chewy meat, marinate it with lemon juice and let it stand overnight. The acidity in the lemon should break down the meat's resistance, making it easier on the mouth!

Simple chicken trick
Put lemon wedges inside the cavity of a whole chicken for flavour.

Brighten up your vegetables!
If you squeeze a little lemon juice over your vegetables while you're steaming them, the colours will stay ultra bright.

Two egg tricks
Dab the eggs with lemon juice before putting them in boiling water to prevent the shells from cracking while cooking. Then add a splash of lemon juice to the boiling water – this will make the eggshells peels off with ease.

Need sour milk?
Some recipes need sour milk or cream, but unless you're a student chances are you'll only have fresh milk in the fridge. If this is the case, squeeze a jot of lemon juice into the milk or cream, and it'll sour nicely.

Power mushrooms
I don't know how this works, but it does. If you want your mushrooms to have an intense taste, squeeze some lemon juice over them as they cook.

Crispy skin

If you want to finish off a roast chicken or duck with really crispy skin, just rub a lemon over it before popping it in the oven.

Poached egg trick

To make sure your poached egg forms a great shape, squeeze a few drops of lemon juice into the boiling water, swirl the water around, then add the egg into the eye of the mini whirlpool.

Okay, that's the little hints and tricks covered. Now let's move on to the main event...the food!

LEMON RECIPES

T here are hundreds and hundreds of recipes that list lemon as one of the ingredients. If I'd published them all, I would have called my work-in-progress *The Lemon Book Volumes 1-27...* and I'd still be typing!

So I've spent hours... no, YEARS... trying these out, and presented here are my favourites.

ASPARAGUS WITH LEMON VINAIGRETTE

Here's what you need:

¼ cup olive oil
2 tb sp freshly squeezed lemon juice
¾ teaspoon fresh thyme leaves, chopped
1 clove garlic, crushed
Salt and black pepper
2 bunches asparagus, washed and trimmed.
(Or to be honest as much asparagus as you want.)

How to prepare:

Mix the olive oil with the lemon juice, thyme, garlic, salt and pepper. Cover the bowl with clingfilm and forget about it for a mo'.

Meanwhile, cook the asparagus in lightly salted boiling water for about 3 minutes. Keep testing the asparagus with a fork – it should be firm but pretty easy to pierce.

Drain the water away and pour cold water over it immediately. Drain off and toss the asparagus with the mixture so it's sort of glazed with it.

Stick on a plate and eat.

Okay, no stars for presentation – but how easy it that? And honestly, this is delicious.

PORK ESCALOPES WITH LEMON SAUCE

What you need:

(for the pork)

4 pieces of pork loin 2½ oz each
100g fresh breadcrumbs
2 unwaxed lemons (you only need the zest – so you can use the rest to
polish the windows while you cook! Only joking...)
1 sprig fresh rosemary
Salt and black pepper
1 heaped tsp wholegrain mustard
50g plain flour
100ml milk
2 free-range eggs

(For the sauce)

100g butter
Olive oil
2 lemons, juice only
125ml white wine

How to prepare:

Cut off any excess fat from the meat, then wrap the slices in clingfilm
and bash them out until they're about 5mm thin.

Place the breadcrumbs in a bowl, and grate the lemon zest into the
bowl with the breadcrumbs (keep the lemons for the sauce).

Add the chopped rosemary to the bowl with the breadcrumbs and lemon zest. Add the salt and pepper... a large pinch from each should do it.

Place the flour in another bowl.

Mix the milk and eggs together in a bowl.

Pat one of the pork escalopes in the flour, then dip it in the egg mixture, then coat in the breadcrumbs. Dip and coat the pork a second time, so that it's really well covered in crumbs. Put on a plate and do the same with the rest.

Heat a large frying pan over a medium heat and melt half the butter with a splash of olive oil.

When the butter is foaming, add the escalopes and fry them until golden-brown on each side.

When they're cooked through, remove from the pan, drain on kitchen paper and keep warm.

To make the sauce, add the rest of the butter to the pan with the juice of the lemons and the wine. Turn up the heat to reduce the sauce by half.

Serve the pork escalopes with the lemon and butter sauce artistically poured over it (or half on the plate, half on the kitchen counter... something I manage to do just about every time).

LEMON CHICKEN

What you need:

(For the chicken)

Chicken thighs or breast fillets
¼ cup corn flour
3tbs water
4 egg yolks
Salt & pepper
Olive oil

(For the sauce)

3tbs flour or rice flour
¼ cup sugar
2 cups water
Juice of 2 to 3 lemons
Chicken stock
2tsp soy sauce
1tsp grated ginger
Salt & pepper
2tsp dry sherry or red wine

How to prepare:

First off, remove the skin from the chicken. Yes, I KNOW it's tasty, but I'm doffing my cap to healthy eating here, and chicken skin has more downsides than upsides, so get rid of it.

Cut the skinless chicken into thick diagonal slices.

Put the flour into a bowl and mix with the water and the lightly beaten egg yolks. Add salt and pepper and give it another stir.

Heat up oil in the frying pan.

Dip the chicken into this mixture, let any excess drip back into the bowl, then slap the chicken strips in the frying pan.

Turn and cook until golden brown, then place the strips on some kitchen roll to soak up excess oil.

Now for the sauce...

Put the flour and sugar in a saucepan, gradually add water and lemon juice, stirring until combined, then stir until sauce boils and thickens.

Add in the chicken stock, soy sauce, salt, pepper and sherry (or red wine if you've got any left after taking "chef's privileges" and having a glass or two while cooking!), reduce heat and simmer for 2-3 minutes.

And that's it – just pour the sauce over the chicken, serve with leeks or broccoli and some boiled potatoes, and eat!

LEMON MERINGUE PIE

What you need:

(For the lemon filling)

1 cup sugar
¼ cup cornstarch
⅛ tsp salt
1 ½ cups water
6 egg yolks, slightly beaten
1 tbsp grated lemon zest
½ cup fresh lemon juice
2 tbsp butter

(For the meringue topping)

1 tbsp cornstarch
⅓ cup water
4 egg whites, room temperature
½ tsp vanilla extract
¼ tsp cream of tartar
½ cup sugar

How to prepare:

Preheat oven to 200°C/180°C fan oven/Gas Mark 6

Prepare pie pastry; dust lightly with flour, wrap in plastic wrap, and refrigerate 30 minutes before rolling.

Right. Now let's start with the meringue:

Mix the cornstarch and water in a small pan. Keep it on a low heat until it simmers, continually stirring until mixture thickens and turns translucent.

Remove from heat.

Get a large bowl and whisk the egg whites with vanilla extract until frothy.

In a small bowl mix cream of tartar and sugar and SLOWLY add to the frothy egg whites. Keep beating and mixing until soft peaks form.

Again, SLOWLY add cornstarch mixture, and keep on mixing until stiff peaks form. You want the meringue top to look like a punk rocker caught out in a light shower.

Now the pastry:

Roll pastry with a floured rolling pin until it's 5cm larger than the dish you're going to stick it in. (You can tell I trained in a French restaurant for years can't you?)

Then lay the pastry in the dish, pressing firmly against bottom and side. Prick the crust at 15mm intervals before baking.

Bake for 15 minutes; reduce oven to 180°C/160°C fan oven/Gas Mark 4. and bake another 10 minutes or until crust is golden brown.

Remove from oven and let it cool.

Reduce oven to 160°C/140°C fan oven/Gas Mark 3, and get ready to put the lemon into the meringue!

Mix the sugar, cornstarch, salt, and water in a saucepan over a low heat and simmer until translucent.

Whisk in the egg yolks gradually. Whisk in lemon zest, lemon juice, and butter.

Remove from heat and pour into your baked pie case.

Get your meringue topping and spread in over the lemon filling. Spread it right to the edge of the pastry.

Stick in the oven for 20 minutes, or until meringue is golden brown. Remove from oven and cool completely before cutting and serving.

Enough for 8 people (or 6 when I'm around).

LEMON MARMALADE RECIPE

What you need:

10 large lemons
4 cups water
4 cups sugar

How to prepare:

Peel off the yellow part of the lemon peel into small strips. (Note: avoid the white pith – you're just after the zest.)

Clean off any of the white pith that's clinging on for dear life.

Take the naked lemons, and cut them diagonally into 6mm slices.

In a heavy non-aluminium pot, mix the lemon peel, sliced fruit and water, cover and stick in the fridge for 4 hours.

Right, once you're back from the pub... sorry, I mean once you've finished tidying the house and spending time with the family, take the mixture out from the fridge and pour it into a heavy saucepan.

Heat the lemon mixture to boiling over a high heat, stirring frequently.

Once it's bubbling away, reduce the heat to low; cover and simmer, stirring occasionally, until lemon mixture is very soft. This will take about an hour.

Add sugar to the lemon mixture and increase heat to medium-high; stir until sugar dissolves.

Boil uncovered, stirring frequently, for about an hour.

Spoon marmalade into hot jars, leaving 1cm space at top of the jars.

Wipe jar rims clean. Seal with lids and bands.

Stick jars in boiling water for 15 minutes. Cool jars on wire rack, then store in a cool dry place.

OLD-FASHIONED LEMONADE

What you need:

Juice of 6 lemons (1 cup)
¾ cup sugar or to taste
4 cups cold water
1 lemon, sliced
Ice cubes

How to prepare:

In a large pitcher, combine lemon juice and sugar; stir to dissolve sugar. Add water, lemon slices, and ice cubes; stir until well blended. Serve in tall glasses over ice.

Honestly, that's it. This is REAL lemonade, not that hideous gassy stuff packed with E-horrors and fake sweeteners. Try this and see which you prefer.

LEMON BARLEY WATER

Ahhhh... lemon barley. It's childhood summers and Wimbledon all rolled into one. (Remember those TV ads...?). It's also incredibly good for you – the barley can help ease urinary and circulatory problems.

The recipe below makes a large jugful.

125g pot barley
2 lemons
50g brown sugar
1.2L water

Wash the barley and put it in your jug along with the lemon rind and sugar. Boil the water and pour over the mixture. When the mixture is cool add the juice of the lemons, strain and then serve.

LEMON MOJITO

2 parts white rum

½ part Cointreau

Juice of ½ lemon juice

Top up soda water

Lemon rind

2 tsp sugar

Muddle (yes, muddle... don't blame me, that's how bartenders speak) lemon juice & sugar. Add the rest and shake. Pour it out into a tall glass, top up with soda water and make it look like a Del Boy drink with some attractive twists of lemon rind.

Lovely-jubbly!

EPILOGUE

A Final Word on Nature's "Cure-All"

I have to say, I'm all lemoned out. But I hope you'll agree it's been worth it...

In fact I hope this book has given you enough ideas to make you buy a bag of lemons the next time you're out shopping. To be honest I had NO idea how many ways lemons and lemon juice could help us when I first started writing my regular free *Good Life Letter* emails (see www.goodlifeletter.co.uk).

I thought they were good for pancakes, good for colds, and that was about it.

But over the last few years I came across so many ways that lemons could protect and improve our health, I just had to get them down in one easy-to-use volume that people could refer to again and again.

And there's really no excuse not to try these tips straight away. Just start with the mojito on page 82, and work backwards!

I hope you've enjoyed this little tome about the power of the lemon.

It really can help you overcome everyday ailments, as well as keeping your body (and your house!) spotless and beautiful.

So the next time you're out shopping at your local grocer's or farmer's market – or even the supermarket if you have to – make sure you stock up on lemons. Because you'll never know when one might come in handy!

Thanks for reading this book, and all the best...

Ray Collins

Ray Collins

www.goodlifeletter.co.uk

PS. Wait a minute! I haven't quite finished yet. See opposite for your free bonus section on another one of nature's miracles...

FREE BONUS SECTION

Discover How to Treat Everyday Health Problems with Ginger

While the humble lemon is a powerful thing indeed, I decided that my book on lemons needed an extra kick. And why not? Why stop at lemons? If you're the kind of brilliant-minded person who would buy this book, you deserve even more secrets, more ideas... more tips and revelations.

I simply needed to find something that was as widespread as lemons, just as cheap, with medicinal properties that were equally as powerful.

It was an easy task, really. Because during my many investigations into natural health remedies for The Good Life Letter (www.goodlifeletter.co.uk) one spice has come up time and time again.

Most people think it's just something you bung into a stir-fry, but they are missing out on another of nature's most effective "cure-alls" for dozens of everyday health problems.

Yes, it's hardly a surprise. As you can tell from my chapter title, I'm talking about ginger.

Thousands of years as an international wonder food

To boffins and anoraks, ginger is known as the root of a plant called *Zingiber officinale*. Great name, huh? This is because *zingiber* is Sanskrit for "shaped like a horn".

They don't mean like a bugle, of course, but the antlers of a deer.

Clearly, Sanskrit isn't our first language, so I'll stick to plain old "ginger". You might like to know that in our delightful language, the knobbly bits are commonly called the "hands".

The history of ginger is as colourful as that of the lemon. It has been used for thousands of years in Indian and Chinese civilisations as a traditional medicine to treat coughing, flu, vomiting, stomach bloating, diarrhoea and rheumatism. The ancient Greeks took ginger from South Asia and used it as an anti-nausea drug. And one of the most famous users of the root was the philosopher Confucius, who claimed that he never dined without the stuff. It must have made all his meals rather zingy.

Then again, he had more important things to think about.

The Chinese have always believed that different forms of ginger have different qualities. For instance, it can be fresh, slivered, dried, powdered and preserved. But don't worry, I'll not only explain the benefits of ginger, but exactly how to use it best at the end of the chapter.

It's really easy and takes virtually no preparation. A matter of making tea, getting out the grater, stirring powder into a drink or swallowing a capsule.

A brief history of ginger

After an illustrious history in China and India, ginger started cropping up everywhere as a medicine. It was taken to the West Indies in the 16th century by the Spanish. In Switzerland, the street in Basel, where traders sold ginger, was called "Ginger Alley".

In England, Henry VIII thought it was a remedy against the plague. The crazy, wife-murdering old goon. And for a while it was used as an aphrodisiac throughout Europe, (not without foundation, as you'll see in a moment).

Eventually the industrial revolution came along, and then the 20th century, and suddenly science had ALL the answers to ALL our problems. Well, supposedly. But of course, we know that disease and chronic illness have not gone away. We're living longer, but we also have to deal with many new problems, chronic illnesses and conditions.

This is why many of us are returning to the solutions that nature offers us

In our mad stampede toward a technological utopia, many natural Eastern remedies and medicines have been pushed to the margins. Many natural secrets have been lost with the passing of generations. In these days of pharmacological drugs, artificial medicines and stiff Westernised thinking, many people have forgotten the power of something as simple and cheap as ginger.

I mean, where's the profits for big business in something like ginger? Can you patent it? Can you claim it as your own?

No, it's just ginger. Grows in the ground. Tough luck, Mr Pharmaceutical Giant.

So the spice has been relegated to a food ingredient. But this is only a tiny part of the miraculous story. History screams at us "GINGER IS GREAT!" I mean, how else could ginger have spread across the globe as a such a powerful and widely-used health remedy? It was hardly down to a marketing campaign was it?

No, it was all about the clear and tangible benefits it offered people. And nothing has changed since the days when Confucius used to chuck it into his dinner.

What's in ginger to make it so powerful?

Ginger contains gingerols and shogaols, which give it a powerful smell. These are also strongly medicinal. Ginger also contains volatile oils, including bisabolene and zingiberene and zingiberol, which give it a strong pungency. It also contains vitamins, especially A and niacin, as well as minerals and amino acids.

All of these are responsible for a large variety of effects, as you're about to read.

I'll shut up now about history and science, and get on with the stuff that actually helps you live a better life. Read on and you'll discover hundreds of ways you can use ginger for a list of everyday ailments.

I hope you'll be shocked, amazed and delighted at the number of uses I've found...

BONUS CHAPTER ONE

The Health Benefits of Ginger

Before you read any further, please can I remind you that you should always seek professional medical advice before you make any severe dietary changes. While ginger is powerful and effective, you should always talk to your doctor if you're worried that you have a serious illness.

Side effects are rare, but excessive doses of ginger in its natural form may cause some mild heartburn. Tell your doctor if you are taking ginger and preparing for surgery of any kind. And finally, don't take it if you are on blood-thinning medications, including aspirin.

Okay, so let's get down to it...

Here are some of the many benefits of ginger. Read them, enjoy them, and afterwards I'll tell you how to buy, store and cook with ginger for maximum effect.

An aid to digestion

First up, ginger is great for digestion. Take some sips of ginger liqueur before eating and you'll stimulate your appetite. Or use it after eating to help everything tick over. Ginger can help get your digestive organs working as they should. The volatile oils in ginger help your body produce more digestive juices and help neutralise your stomach acids.

Not surprising, then, that many rich ancient Romans took ginger as commonly as people take Alka-Seltzer today. They would swallow it with their meals as a digestive aid. That and a bunch of grapes, of course, brought by a beautiful serving wench, if those old "Sword and Sandals" films are close to the truth.

In the 18th century, ginger was given to people after meals. It was even a popular sweet in North America during colonial times. So you see, this isn't new information. But it's not well-known information. Which is a shame, really.

The German government's Commission E (a food standards agency) recommends ginger on a daily basis for digestive problems. They suggest eating 2g-4g a day. This is like swallowing a 2.5cm piece of ginger, or 500mg-1,000mg of ginger supplements.

Protection from parasites

Ginger, it has been claimed, can also help ward off ulcers and protect you from parasites that try to enter your intestines.

In Japan, pickled ginger is traditionally eaten with sushi because of zingibain, a parasite-killing chemical that's been shown to kill the anisakid worm, occasionally found in raw fish.

Treat inflammation and arthritis

Many health care professionals today use ginger to help treat health problems associated with inflammation, such as arthritis. In a 1992 study, ginger was given to people suffering from muscle pain. It resulted in at least some improvement for all of the subjects. In that same study, 75% of the test subjects who had experienced rheumatoid arthritis or osteoarthritis said they felt substantial relief.

One way to use ginger for inflammation is to drink a fresh ginger juice extract, or tea, 2g-4g daily. (I'll explain how to make teas and juices properly later on.)

You can also use it as a topical agent. What you do is rub ginger oil directly onto a painful joint. Or you can take some fresh ginger root, put it in a warm poultice or compress and apply it to the affected joints.

Try seeking out an essential oil made from ginger, or make your own (see more details on page 100 under Naturally relieve stress). You can use this oil in massages to treat rheumatism, lumbago, or for bone injuries.

Tip: it will combine well with almond oil, juniper or eucalyptus oils.

Boost your blood circulation

Ginger is known to be a thinning agent for the blood. This means it is very good for your circulation. It is known to be a treatment for many illnesses characterized by poor circulation, including Raynaud's syndrome.

It can work very well with cayenne pepper, which has a reputation of being an emergency aid in a heart attack! (That sounds weird, but it's true.) Cayenne stimulates the heart, regulates the blood flow and strengthens your arteries and capillaries.

A tip: mix cayenne pepper with fresh ginger. This helps boost those tiny capillaries which receives little or no blood flow. Fresh ginger and fresh cayenne peppers work best because they have higher amounts of bioflavonoids and vitamins.

Try cutting up the root, dicing it finely and adding it to soups, casseroles and other dishes. Or treat yourself to some Chinese,

Vietnamese and Thai recipes. Many of their dishes are packed with ginger.

I'll also show you a pretty decent juice recipe in a moment, but hold your horses, here's another powerful benefit of ginger...

Help in the fight against heart disease

The gingerol and shogaol in ginger, it is claimed by some experts, may be able to ward off heart attacks and strokes by preventing the platelet clumping or stickiness that can lead to blood clots and atherosclerosis. This is a disease of the arteries where the inner lining of the arterial walls thicken because of fatty material.

In a few studies, ginger has been shown to be almost as effective as aspirin in preventing blood clots. According to Danish researchers, ginger is better at blocking the blood clots than even garlic or onion. The compound in ginger known as "gingerol" is very similar to that of aspirin, which has long been used to thin the blood.

Ayurvedic doctors also suggest that eating a bit of ginger every day will help to prevent heart attack.

But this is still early days for research of this kind, so never rely on ginger. Simply understand its potential and pack your diet full of fresh fruit and vegetables, with healthy doses of natural, fresh ginger.

If it doesn't ward off strokes and heart attacks to the extent that the experts claim, then it certainly won't do you any harm. A wholesome diet of fresh, raw vegetables can never be a bad thing.

Ease menstrual cramps

Ginger is packed with pain-relieving compounds and anti-cramping compounds, making it a very reliable treatment for menstrual pain. Many women swear by it. But often commercial ginger teas are far too weak to deal with the problem quickly or powerfully enough.

Steep two tablespoons of freshly shredded ginger in hot water, two to three times daily. You can also pop some ginger oil or a few slices of the fresh stuff into water and either drink it, or inhale it. Take it on a daily basis for a week to get the cumulative effects.

Or here's another tip I've found...

Make a hot ginger-tea compress and lay it on your lower stomach. This should help relax your muscles and ease the cramping. To make the compress, simply boil 170g of ginger in a pint of water for 15 minutes. Now dip an absorbent cloth or towel into the solution. Wrap it in another cloth and press it onto your stomach.

Treat bloating and flatulence

These days, our Western diets are very rich, laden with carbohydrates and additives. Junk food is rife, as is binge drinking and overeating. So no surprise then that we are a windy society. And I'm not talking about the cliff-top breeze.

Luckily, ginger can help you deal with any embarrassing and smelly flatulence problems. Take 2g-4g of fresh ginger root daily. That's the same as 0.25g-1.0g of powdered root. Or you can take the liquid extract.

Another way to deal with it is to soak fresh ginger slices in lime juice and chew on them after each meal. You may look a bit like a cow chewing the cud, but at least you won't fart like one.

Treat morning sickness and nausea

At least three trials in the past have found ginger to be more effective than a placebo in controlling morning sickness. It may also prevent the nausea you get from surgery and chemotherapy.

Why? Well, according to Japanese researchers, ginger can block your body's vomit reflex. This makes it an obvious remedy for morning sickness. In one test I read about, 19 out of 27 women who use ginger to stop sickness found that the problem became less frequent in just four days of treatment.

Mark Stengler, N.D, author of *A Handbook of Natural Remedies* advises that women shouldn't take more than 1g daily of ginger during their pregnancy. And that there is no reason to continue taking ginger after your morning sickness has passed.

To prevent vomiting, take 1g of powdered ginger (½ tsp) or its equivalent, every 4 hours as needed, or two ginger capsules (1g), three times daily.

You can also chew a 7g piece of fresh ginger whenever necessary.

Fight the symptoms of motion sickness

Ginger has long been known to prevent and treat motion sickness. A popular drug for motion sickness is known as Dramamine ™. But tests in 1982, reported in *The Lancet*, showed that ginger may even be superior to this drug for treating motion sickness.

In 1994 some researchers tested a bunch of people on a whale watching trip. They were given 250mg of ginger and found that the effect was just as powerful as with artificial drugs. The best thing about using ginger for motion sickness is that it doesn't have nasty side effects like drowsiness.

Another more amusing test was done by the American Pytotherapy Research Laboratory in Salt Lake City.

They took a bunch of students who often suffered from motion sickness and spun them around for six minutes. It doesn't say how they were spun in the medical journal I read, but I like to think it was on one of those NASA g-force machines.

Anyway, one group was given Dramamine™. The other group was given ginger. The group who took the ginger were able to cope with the spinning for six minutes, while the other group had to give up after 4 ½ minutes.

Try taking a quarter of a teaspoon of ginger root 20 minutes before a car trip, or any other transport for that matter, estimate that this should give you between three and five hours of relief from motion sickness. A good idea is to make a cup of boiling ginger tea and keep it in a flask for the journey. Whenever you feel the motion sickness coming on, simply take a sip.

Hey, and it tastes lovely, too.

Treat vertigo

In the same way that ginger helps people who have motion sickness, it can also treat vertigo. In 1986, the effect of powdered ginger root was studied in 8 healthy volunteers in a double-blind crossover placebo trial.

Ginger root reduced induced vertigo significantly more than the placebo did.

Reduce the pain of headaches and migraines

Danish researchers have found that ginger can block the effects of prostaglandin – this substance can inflame the blood vessels in your brain and lead to migraines. Ginger has antihistamine and anti-inflammatory properties, which may also be a reason for its effectiveness.

In my research I found a bit of anecdotal information about ginger and migraines. Apparently, a woman in Denmark took 500mg to 600mg of powdered ginger in water when she saw the first sign of a migraine. She claimed she found relief within 30 minutes.

For some people, the worst thing about migraine is the nausea that comes with it. As you've already seen, ginger is a powerful remedy for nausea, so you can take it in the same ways, detailed preiously.

Fresh ginger may be the most effective form of the spice for preventing migraines. This is because the pungent oils in raw ginger have the most active properties. Try eating a 7mm slice of fresh ginger root, every day. In the event of a migraine, some experts will recommend you take 5g-6g of powdered ginger at the first sign. Add it to a glass of water and then drink. Repeat every couple of hours up to six times a day, as required.

You can also take it tincture form. A 'tincture' is an extract in an alcohol solution in the amount of 1.5ml-3ml, three times daily. Another way, you can use ginger for a headaches is to combine powdered ginger and cold water to make a paste. Simply rub it on your forehead and temples, and then have a nice lie down.

Clear your sinuses

If your headache is more of a dull face ache that causes pounding and pain around the eyes, cheeks and forehead, then it may be sinus-related. Try stirring two to three cloves of garlic and two to three slices of ginger into boiling water.

Steep this heady concoction for five to 15 minutes and then drink. Make sure you breathe in the steam and relax.

Ward off the threat of cancer

Some studies show that ginger can prevent the growth of the fungi that produce aflatoxin, a strong carcinogen. Ginger also contains compounds that protect the fats in your body from being attacked by free radicals. These are the beasties that can trigger cancer, so the more protection you have, the better.

In 2003, tests at the University of Minnesota showed that gingerol – the compound which gives ginger its flavour – could slow the growth of human tumours in mice.

Dr Ann Bode, who led the research, said:

"Plants of the ginger family have been credited with therapeutic and preventive powers and have been reported to have anti-cancer activity... these results strongly suggest that ginger compounds may be effective chemopreventive and/or chemotherapeutic agents for colorectal carcinomas."

In words you and I can understand, she believes there's enough evidence to suggest that ginger can help protect you from – and even treat – cancer.

Even more recently, in 2006, laboratory studies in the US showed that powdered root ginger could be as effective as chemotherapy for treating ovarian cancer. When research-grade ginger was applied to ovarian cancer cells in Petri dishes, it proved effective for stopping cell growth.

Again, it's early days for this kind of research, but there's no harm in adding some healthy doses of fresh ginger to your meals, or taking it as a supplement.

Treat coughs and colds

Ginger has been known to reduce the time it takes to get over fevers and coughs. It is also a natural decongestant and antihistamine. This is because ginger root – as well as tamarind – contains volatile oils that warm and soothe our air passages when we breathe. So if you have a cough, cold or bronchitis, then ginger is a must have for your medicine cabinet.

Here's a homemade recipe to make the most of these ingredients...

Cut a ginger root into thin slices. Add a few handfuls of tamarind leaves to a pot and add the sliced ginger on top. Add two glasses of water. Boil for 30 minutes and strain through some muslin or teatowl. Pour out a glass of the liquid and add half a glass of sugar. Then boil until it turns into a syrup. Cool the mixture, then stir in the juice of three limes.

Hey presto, your 100% natural home made medicine, packed with the power of ginger.

Another less elaborate preparation that I personally use is to make a hot toddy with ginger. Simply squeeze half a lemon into a mug, add two teaspoons of honey and four or five slices of root ginger. Now add an (optional) splash of Scotch and then fill with water. My wife tells me off for making these with whisky when I haven't even got a cold. That's how good they taste.

Finally, in India, they give children ginger tea to deal with the problems of whooping cough, so it's also worth a try.

Naturally relieve stress

Not many people know about ginger as a stress relief aid, but it makes sense, if you think about it. We've already seen that ginger can relieve inflammation, kill pain, soothe headaches and reduce nausea, all of which cause stress, or come with stress.

It also makes a relaxing massage oil. All you do is mix one part freshly grated ginger to five parts olive oil in a clear glass jar. Leave to cool at room temperature for 24 hours. Then you strain and bottle it.

Or try a soothing ginger bath. Put $\frac{1}{8}$ cup of grated ginger under a warm, running tap. Get in and crank up the heat from the tap until it's as hot as you can handle. Then climb in bed and switch off for 45 minutes.

Freshen your mouth

It has been said that a small piece of ginger, slowly chewed and sucked in the mouth can relieve toothache and mouth ulcers.

Ease a sore throat

If you are suffering from a sore throat or swollen tonsils, here's another powerful little secret. You simply mix one teaspoon of dried ginger, half a lemon and a teaspoon of honey. Then add a cup of boiling water. Wait for it to cool down. Gargle with it for 30 seconds.

Help lower cholesterol levels

I'm not going to pretend for a minute that ginger on its own can be an instant cure for high levels of bad cholesterol, but there is some evidence that it can help. A study has shown that just 5g of dried ginger every a day can slow the production of triglycerides and LDL (bad) cholesterol in the liver.

Cinnamon also has blood-thinning properties that can help towards lowering cholesterol levels. So try stiring a teaspoon of cinnamon and a quarter teaspoon of ginger into hot water. Leave for five minutes. Drink once every morning and evening.

A powerful hangover remedy

If you fancy a hair of the dog, try this hangover remedy. You juice up six carrots, two apples and a good-sized chunk of fresh ginger. Chuck this into a juicer or blender and add a shot of vodka at the end. Drink it down and think very hard about your terrible, irresponsible behaviour.

Or if you're feeling hungover, ill, hungry, depressed and starved of nutrients, here's one for you. Blend some raw broccoli, garlic juice, onions and ginger.

I can't imagine a hangover will hang around too much longer after drinking that.

A seasonal air freshener

As I've already explained in my chapters about lemons, many modern air fresheners and household chemicals are very bad for you indeed. Those adverts on the telly for airfresheners are very convincing, but you can actually make your house smell gorgeous – and much nicer than with any chemical – with the help of ginger.

This is especially good in winter and around Christmas time. All you do is add cloves, orange peel, ground cinnamon, vanilla extract and fresh ginger to a pot of water, and simmer the mixture slowly on the stove.

Your house will gradually fill with a gorgeous, natural, soothing scent.

A sex life booster

Ginger is very stimulating for your whole body. It can wake you up, give you an energy boost, and immediately stimulate your blood flow and circulation. This is crucial for male and female sexual enjoyment. Not surprising, then, that a couple of hundred years ago it was considered a bit of an aphrodisiac.

Here's what to do if you need a little "love injection". Simply take 28g of fresh ginger and juice it up with quarter of a large watermelon. Drink and go for it.

Spice up a boring meal

Finally, of course, there's the blindingly obvious use for ginger: for cooking tasty meals and desserts. It's an aromatic and powerful addition to any meal. You can grate it, slice it, chuck it into stir-fries. But I won't go into these here, as I'm no Nigella Lawson. I'm a man, for one thing.

All I'll say is that cooking with ginger is something you should definitely look into. Not just for the health benefits, but for the taste. And a final tip, when you use ginger, make sure you extract the juice or the grated pulp of the ginger root. Try using a good grater or a garlic press to get the most out of the pulp.

BONUS CHAPTER TWO

How to Make Ginger Tea

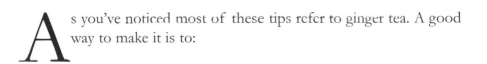

As you've noticed most of these tips refer to ginger tea. A good way to make it is to:

1. Slice a 5cm chunk of fresh ginger root into very thin slices
2. Boil 4 cups worth of water
3. Stew the ginger and water in a teapot or on a covered pot on the hob for 15 minutes
4. Strain and serve
5. Add honey and/or lemon to enhance the taste.

Or for a quicker method, grate 3 teaspoons of ginger to a cup of boiling water. Easy.

Finally, I'll round off this journey through ginger, with a few tips about buying and storing it.

BONUS CHAPTER THREE

Tips on Buying and Storing Ginger

You'll find ginger almost anywhere these days. The best place to look is your local market. Your corner shop will probably stock some. And of course, the ubiquitous supermarket will stock it.

When shopping for ginger, look for smooth skin with a fresh, spicy fragrance. Avoid pieces with wrinkled flesh, as this means it's past its prime. Also avoid buying ginger with mould or soft spots. The tubers should be firm and heavy. In terms of strength and potency, African and India ginger are the most powerful types.

Your ginger root should be kept in a cool, dry place, at around 5°C. You can refrigerate it in plastic for up to a week. Or if you want to keep it longer, peel it and cover it with sherry vinegar before popping it in the fridge. Or freeze it for up to three months.

You can also get ginger in the form of an extract or pill. Take ginger capsules with a glass of water. It's okay to take half a teaspoon to three-quarters of a teaspoon of fresh, powdered ginger three times a day.

Try not to eat ginger root more than three times a day. High doses may damage the stomach lining and could eventually lead to ulcers. Commercially sold ginger tea is a lot weaker so you can drink that many more times if you like.

For more information on this, or any other natural remedies, find out more at **www.goodlifeletter.co.uk**. I also offer a FREE weekly newsletter packed with advice, remedies, recipes and tips.

All the best of health to you!

Afterword

I hope you enjoyed this book. For more information like this, please go to www.goodlifeletter.co.uk and you'll see hundreds of ideas, tips and alternative health remedies for FREE.

I also recommend you try out my FREE twice-weekly email service, *The Good Life Letter*. In a fun and entertaining way, I investigate everything from easing back pain, managing migraines and cleaning your arteries... to protecting yourself against heart, bowel, lung and liver diseases.

Go to www.goodlifeletter.co.uk, enter your email address, and I'll do the rest. Please understand that I respect your email privacy and won't pass on your details to anyone else.

All the best

Ray Collins
The Good Life Letter
www.goodlifeletter.co.uk

NOTES

NOTES

NOTES

NOTES

NOTES

NOTES

NOTES

NOTES

NOTES

NOTES

ADC 9/15